So you <u>really</u> want to ....

Geography

Book One
Answer Book

James Dale-Adcock

Series Editor: Simon Lewis

ISEB
Independent Schools
Examinations Board

www.galorepark.co.uk

GALORE PARK

Published by Galore Park Publishing Ltd
19/21 Sayers Lane, Tenterden, Kent TN30 6BW

www.galorepark.co.uk

Text copyright © James Dale-Adcock 2008

The right of James Dale-Adcock to be identified as the author of this Work
has been asserted by him in accordance with sections 77 and 78 of the
Copyright, Designs and Patents Act 1988.

Typography by Typetechnique, London
Illustrations by Ian Moores

Printed and bound by CPI Antony Rowe, Chippenham

ISBN-13: 978 1 902984 73 5

First published 2008

Details of other Galore Park publications are available at
www.galorepark.co.uk

ISEB Revision Guides, publications and examination papers may also be
obtained from Galore Park.

Contents

Introduction

The answers provided in this book are by no means prescriptive. Some topics, such as Location knowledge and Mapwork, lend themselves to specific 'right' or 'wrong' answers. However, many areas of Geography are subjective, and a range of answers are feasible if sound reasoning is given. Although it is not always practical, marking with the pupil present is good practice and can be a method of shared learning for the teacher or parent and child, as well as a perfect opportunity for reward.

If a pupil provides an answer not given in this book it is always wise to ask them how they came to their conclusion. This may be more pertinent to the Extension questions which are designed for more able pupils and which, by their nature, may elicit a wider range of responses. Some suggestions have been given to the kind of extended answers pupils may give, but these are by no means exhaustive.

James Dale-Adcock
2008

Chapter 1: Geographical skills

Part A: Mapwork skills

1.1 The OS map and using grid references

Exercise 1A

1. (a) 9488   Multiple answers possible, e.g. motorway, river, railway, floodplain.
   (b) 9590   Multiple answers possible, e.g. golf course, dual carriageway.
   (c) 9892   Multiple answers possible, e.g. electricity transmission line, non-coniferous wood, footpath.
   (d) 9691   Multiple answers possible, e.g. railway station, roundabout, motorway junction.

2. 9592 (x 2)   9390   9490   9392

3. (a) 967883   train station
   (b) 946903   school
   (c) 989897   farm
   (d) 932927   hospital

4. 976925   965892   980884

5. (a) 952905   car
   (b) 933907   boat
   (c) 966883   train
   (d) 933883   by foot

Extension question

6.

933918	936910
934922	954928
935925	936925
937917	941920
937923	937925
942882	966882 x 2
943918	944916 x 2
965881	966885
966887 x 2	941904
976925	941882
984889	979904

1.2 Identifying direction and measuring distances

Exercise 1B

1. (a) north-west
   (b) south-east

2. (a) 8 km
   (b) east

3. (a) 6 km
   (b) 8 km
   (c) Pupils may describe various routes for their journey to the zoo. One option follows:

   Take the minor road north from Whitwell to Godshill. Turn right in Godshill onto the A3020 travelling east. When you reach the village of Sandford turn left towards Summersbury following the National Cycle Network in a northerly direction. Turn left onto the A3056 and take the first left to the zoo.

4. (a) 3.5 km
   (b) south-east

5. (a) 3 km
   (b) north-east

Extension question

6. (a) 317 degrees
   (b) 220 degrees
   (c) 45 degrees

1.3 Height and shape of land on OS maps

Exercise 1C

1. (a) From the north because the contour lines are packed tightly together making this route the shortest but the steepest.
   (b) From the south because the contour lines are spread furthest apart from this direction making a route from the south the longest and most gentle.
   (c) 108 metres

2. (a) 54 metres
   (b) hill/flat top hill

3.   (a) 235 metres
      (b) 567801 This is the highest point in the area because it is marked by a
          triangulation pillar.

Extension question

4.   Multiple answers are possible, but pupils should have drawn a sketch similar to
      the one below which is for grid square 1581

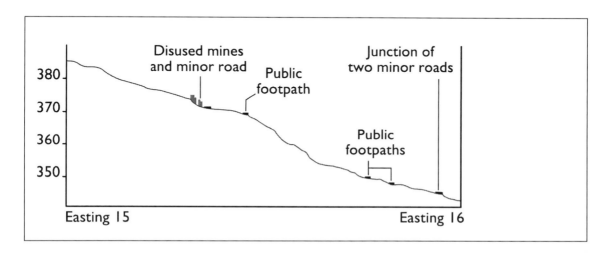

Chapter 2: Environmental issues

2.1 What is the environment and why does it need protecting?

Exercise 2A

1. The environment is the term used to describe the **landscape** and **atmosphere** of a given area and includes the wildlife, both plants and animals, which make the area their home (**habitat**).

2.

Local	National	Global
recycling	urban sprawl endangered species	global warming/ endangered species

3. (a) The protection and preservation of the environment for people today and tomorrow.

   (b) Multiple answers are possible, for example:

   On a local scale – protecting local wildlife habitats from building developments which is the job of the planning officers on the local council.

   On a national scale – preventing industry from polluting our rivers, the atmosphere or sea, which is the job of a government department called the Environment Agency.

   On a global scale – our atmosphere needs protecting from greenhouse gases such as carbon dioxide which trap heat in the atmosphere around the Earth, resulting in global warming. It is the collective responsibility of the governments of all the world's countries, particularly those with a great deal of industry, to reduce emissions of carbon dioxide.

4. (a) Global warming is the artificial heating of our atmosphere, caused by the emission of gases such as carbon dioxide into the atmosphere from cars, aeroplanes and coal burning power stations. This pollution has created an ever thickening blanket of gases within the atmosphere which traps the sun's rays as they are reflected back off the earth, thereby causing small but significant rises in global atmospheric temperature.

(b) Multiple answers are possible, for example:

Society and individuals in society who have a large 'carbon footprint' generated from car use and domestic energy use.

Some pupils may wish to add further personal interpretations, for example:

Governments which encourage the use of fossil fuels as the principal form of energy production.

5.   Agreement between different nations, such as the USA, UK, China, South Africa and Australia has seen Antarctica and its unique wildlife designated a global natural reserve under the *Protocol on Environmental Protection to the Antarctic Treaty (1991)*. This means that the land and sea resources are protected from destructive activities.

Extension question

6.   Pupils will use their own research and personal interpretations to give various answers, for example:

On a local scale – distributing leaflets to explain the benefits of recycling and encouraging residents to recycle as much as possible.

On a national scale – governments can educate younger members of society about the environment by making sure it is taught in schools.

On a global scale – the media and celebrities can be used to highlight issues such as endangered species, deforestation and global warming.

2.2 Case study: Sustainable development in the Peak District National Park

Exercise 2B

1.   National Parks in Britain were set up to conserve and enhance the natural beauty, wildlife and cultural heritage. Further to this they were designed to promote opportunities for the understanding and enjoyment of their special qualities.

2.   The Peak District is the nearest and most accessible National Park for many urban dwellers living in the Midlands and in the north-west of England. In fact, over 17 million people live within 60 miles of the Park. It is the nearest large area of countryside to large **urban areas** such as Manchester, Sheffield, Bradford,

Derby and Nottingham. The high population density of the immediate region around the park, coupled with easy road access via the M1 and M6 **motorways**, means on average the Park receives up to 10,000 cars on its narrow roads each day. This figure is significantly increased in the summer months and on weekends and bank holidays particularly in **honeypot** locations such as Bakewell. Further to this, unlike many other National Parks in Britain, the Peak District National Park is well served by public transport.

3. (a) A disagreement between two or more people (or groups of people) over the use of land. For example, conflict between tourists and farmers in National Parks.

   (b) Multiple answers are possible, for example:

   Conflict between tourists and local residents:

   Wealthy outsiders may buy houses in the national parks to use as holiday homes, reducing the already limited housing available for locals.

   Conflict between tourists and farmers:

   Tourists threaten free grazing farming by trampling grazing pasture and by walking or mountain biking off the signed footpaths. Often, traditional dry stone walls, which are of cultural importance, are knocked down as people scramble over them and gates are left open, causing livestock to escape. As the landscape does not look like what most tourists perceive to be a farm, they treat it as common land and often believe they should be able to roam freely.

4. Although tourist money often provides locals with jobs, there has been an increasing trend in recent years of wealthy outsiders buying local houses to use as holiday homes. This reduces the already limited housing available for locals and pushes the housing prices up so they often cannot afford housing and have to move away from the area. Because many homes are holiday homes, the permanent population of villages in National Parks is low and often cannot support basic services such as post offices or banks.

5. (a) Pupils will have their own ideas about this from research, but could include the following examples:

   Planting evergreen (coniferous) trees around quarries helps to absorb both the noise and dust created by quarrying. These trees also create a pleasing visual barrier preventing visual pollution from the quarry.

(b) Park wardens monitor tourist activities in National Parks and discourage people from scrambling over walls.

Pupils may also have their own ideas including the following:

Providing clear signs and creating sties or swing gates for walkers to cross farmland will help reduce the number of tourists scrambling over dry stone walls.

Extension question

6. Multiple answers are possible, for example:

Only allowing cars to enter the park on weekdays. This would prevent the huge build up in congestion and resulting pollution that occurs at weekends but may reduce the income for hotels and other businesses which make most of their money at these peak times.

Preventing further development of hotel accommodation within honeypots such as Bakewell. This would stabilise the capacity of the Peak District National Park to accommodate overnight visitors but restrict further facilities being developed in honeypots that could benefit the locals as well as visitors.

Pupils may have their own ideas from research they have undertaken, for example:

Charging people for entry. This would reduce the number of visitors but perhaps deny access to the Park for poorer communities who are at most need of a break from urban areas.

Park and Ride scheme. This could be offered in conjunction with the park's extensive public transport system and would keep cars out of the park.

2.3 Case study: Sustainable development in Tsavo National Park in Kenya

Exercise 2C

1. (a) Wealthy countries such as Britain, the USA and many European countries are called More Economically Developed Counties or **MEDCs**. Poorer countries such as Indonesia and Bolivia are called Less Economically developed countries or **LEDCs**. Generally speaking, most Asian, African and South American counties are LEDCs and most European, North American and Oceania countries are MEDCs.

(b) Multiple answers are possible, for example:
MEDCs – United Kingdon, USA, Germany, Japan, Australia.
LEDCs – Bolivia, Chad, Mozambique, Afghanistan, Indonesia.

2. (a) Kenya has large areas of savannah grassland, the habitat for wildlife such as elephants, rhinos, buffalo and lions and leopards (the 'Big Five'), which tourists come to see on safaris. The beautiful Great Rift Valley overlooked by Mount Kenya provides a challenging environment for walkers and mountain climbers. Sandy beaches that line the Indian Ocean coastline attract tourists in search of relaxing holidays. Finally, Kenya's coastline has the added attraction of coral reefs which tourists may also choose to visit for scuba diving or snorkelling holidays.

   (b) Seasonal employment is employment that is only available for part of the year, for example when tourists visit an area because of the hot weather or during the ski season. Tourism jobs in Kenya are not seasonal because of Kenya's equatorial climate, which ensures sunny and hot weather, which attracts tourists, throughout the year.

3. Multiple answers are possible, for example:

   The safari was amazing! To begin with we were in the east of the Tsavo National Park where we saw all of the 'Big Five' including elephants drinking at Mudana Rock, a large permeable rock formation. Later we moved to the west of the park which is more mountainous and has lakes, swamps and grassland. We saw rhinos in the savanna and, at Mizima Springs, went on a glass-bottom boat ride to look at the hippos.

4.

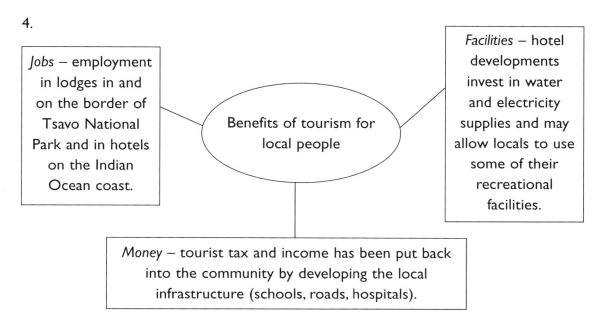

Jobs – employment in lodges in and on the border of Tsavo National Park and in hotels on the Indian Ocean coast.

Benefits of tourism for local people

Facilities – hotel developments invest in water and electricity supplies and may allow locals to use some of their recreational facilities.

Money – tourist tax and income has been put back into the community by developing the local infrastructure (schools, roads, hospitals).

5. (a) Multiple answers are possible, for example:

As tourist numbers have increased over recent years so has the level of soil erosion caused by safari vans driving across the dry soil instead of keeping to roads and tracks in Tsavo National Park. Soil erosion kills vegetation and if it continues will threaten the habitat that supports the wild animals that tourists come to Kenya to visit in the first place. To reduce the impact of soil erosion and other environmental impacts of tourism, park wardens enforce a strict code of conduct for visitors.

(b) Multiple answers are possible, for example:

Although tourism creates permanent jobs in Tsavo National Park and other areas, the better-paid jobs such as hotel managers, childcare supervisors and water sports instructors rarely go to local people. This is because the multi-national hotel chains are run by and catering for Americans and Europeans. The Kenyan government actively promotes Kenyan-owned hotels in order to address this issue.

Extension question

6. Pupils' answers should be based on the premise that while attracting vast numbers of tourists is good for Kenya's economy in the short term, it may harm the economy in the long term because safari vans are causing significant soil erosion and coral reefs are being damaged. If this continues, the wildlife that tourists come to Kenya to see will not exist as its habitat will have been destroyed.

2.4 Scholarship: Sustainable development

Exercise 2D

1. (a) Sustainable development is the idea of protecting our planet's environment and resources for future generations by not using up or damaging resources that cannot be replaced.

    (b) Multiple answers are possible, for example:
    - increasing the use of public transport
    - increasing the number of households involved in recycling

2.

Target: Increase the number of people working from home.
Aim: Reduce the use of cars and resulting congestion/pollution.
Method: Investing in information technology (IT) and promoting flexible working hours within local businesses.

Target: Increase the number of residents working in Kirklees.
Aim: Prevent people using their cars to commute out of Kirklees.
Method: Providing grants to encourage business to locate in Kirklees rather than elsewhere in the region.

Kirklees Metropolitan Council responses to Agenda 21

Target: Reduce congestion.
Aim: Reduce the pollution and relating problems caused by congestion.
Method: Possible schemes include building bypasses, charging high rates for town centre parking and allowing cars which have more than one occupant to use bus lanes or the hard-shoulder of motorways such as the M62.

Target: Increase the use of public transport.
Aim: Reduce congestion and pollution.
Method: Invest in railways, bus services, and possible tram networks for larger settlements.

3.   Multiple answers are possible, for example:

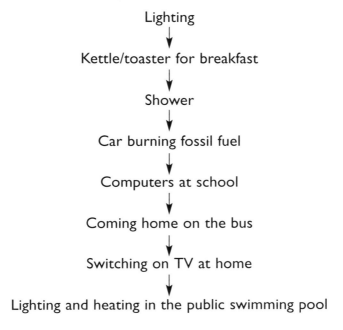

Lighting
↓
Kettle/toaster for breakfast
↓
Shower
↓
Car burning fossil fuel
↓
Computers at school
↓
Coming home on the bus
↓
Switching on TV at home
↓
Lighting and heating in the public swimming pool

4.   (a) Pupils answers may vary, but should include the following information:

Renewable resources will never run out. These resources tend to be expensive to set up but do not pollute the environment in the way that non-renewable resources do.

Non-renewable resources can only be used once and will therefore at some stage run out. They pollute the environment.

The three **fossil fuels** are coal, oil and natural gas. They have taken millions of years to form and cannot be replaced once they are used. Fossil fuels pollute the environment when they are used and are rapidly running out.

     (b) Ultimately non-renewable resources will run out, some sooner than others, so renewable resources must be developed in the long term. Burning fossil fuels such as coal and oil emits carbon dioxide, which is contributing to global warming, therefore encouraging the use of renewables in the short term is also necessary.

5. Energy is generated from water by using the force of falling water to power turbines and a generator. At Dinorwig, the power station was built on the edge of Llyn Peris, and a reservoir was created higher up the mountain from the power station. The water flows down to power the six large turbines and, during off-peak electricity periods, some of the electricity which has been generated is used to pump the water back up to the reservoir. The remaining power that is created from the powerful flow is used fed into the local power system at times of peak need. Other HEP stations generate the pressure needed to turn the turbines by building high dam walls to bridge the valleys of fast-flowing rivers in highland areas. The area behind the dam wall will then be flooded to create a reservoir which can be used to supply fresh water to the local and even neighbouring regions, as well as being used for tourist and leisure activities such as fishing, water skiing and sailing.

Extension question

6. Multiple answers and examples are possible, for example:

In order to preserve our environment and resources for future generations, schemes to encourage sustainable development need to be developed at all levels. This will create a sense of environmental concern amongst the world's citizens whatever their role in society.

At a local level, Kirklees Metropolitan Council have reduced the number of commuters by giving grants for businesses to locate in the town centre. This will reduce commuting to cities further away, and therefore reduce carbon dioxide emissions. Governments of MEDCs have encouraged sustainable development at a national level by building HEP power stations (such as Dinorwig in North Wales) to supply electricity instead of fossil fuel burning power stations.

The Rio Earth Summit of 1992 encouraged all countries to farm in a sustainable manner. LEDCs such as Indonesia have adopted crop rotation in response to the summit's suggestions to reduce soil erosion.

Chapter 3: Tectonic processes

3.1 Where do we experience earthquakes and volcanoes?

Exercise 3A

1. Nearly all earthquakes and volcanoes occur at **plate boundaries** where two sections of the earth's crust meet. There are three types of plate boundary.

    At a **constructive boundary,** two oceanic plates move apart creating undersea volcanoes such as along the Mid-Atlantic Ridge.

    At a **destructive boundary**, the plates move towards each other. When an oceanic plate moves towards a continental plate, the oceanic plate slides underneath the continental plate setting off earthquakes due to friction followed by volcanic eruptions due to increased pressure in the mantle (e.g. volcanoes in the Andes mountains). When two continental plates move towards one another, this is called a **collision boundary**. This creates buckled mountain ranges such as the Himalayas, where there are occasional earthquakes.

    At a **conservative boundary**, plates slide past each other, creating friction that can build up to create earthquakes along fault lines such as the San Andreas fault in California, USA.

2. Continental plates are **thicker**, **older** and made of **less dense** rock than oceanic plates. Oceanic plates are **thinner**, **newer** and made of **more dense** rock than continental plates. These differences mean that when the two types of plate are forced together the oceanic plate slides underneath the continental plate in a place called the subduction zone.

3. (a) At a destructive plate boundary, the plates move towards each other. When an **oceanic plate** moves towards a **continental plate**, this gives rise to volcanoes and earthquakes. As the oceanic plate is thinner but denser than the continental plate it begins to slide underneath the continental plate. As it slides down into the **mantle**, considerable **friction** occurs, leading to earthquakes in an area called the **subduction zone**. This zone can be some way out to sea, in which case large earthquakes in the subduction zone can lead to tsunamis. The oceanic plate melts as it enters the mantle and after time this causes **pressure** to build up in the mantle which is periodically released through the crust as a volcanic eruption.

(b) The **Andes Mountains** contain several active volcanes and experience a high frequency of earthquakes due to the oceanic **Nazca plate** sliding underneath the continental **South American plate** along the west coast of the South American continent.

4. At **collision boundaries** two continental plates are forced into one another. As both plates are of the same thickness and density, neither will slide beneath the other but they buckle up or **fold** instead. This buckling up causes frequent earthquakes and the formation of high mountain ranges.

5. (a)

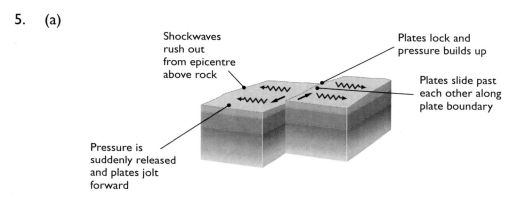

(b) Volcanoes do not occur at conservative or collision plate boundaries because there is no opportunity or cause for magma to rise to the surface at either of these plate boundaries.

Extension question

6. At a constructive plate boundary, the lava is under pressure from the ocean above and is not rich in dissolved gases so eruptions tend to be of a constant nature and not very violent. Volcanic eruptions at destructive plate boundaries tend to be violent because seawater and marine life from the ocean floor are taken down into the mantle and turned into hydrogen and nitrogen. These gases mix with the pressurised magma in the mantle and lead to large and spectacular eruptions. The **Andes mountains** contain several active volcanoes and experience a high frequency of earthquakes due to the oceanic **Nazca plate** sliding underneath the continental **South American plate**.

3.2 Case study: Earthquake in an LEDC, Indonesia 2004

Exercise 3B

1. Draw a well-labelled diagram to illustrate what led to the earthquake and resulting tsunami that devastated the Indian Ocean coastline on Boxing Day 2004.

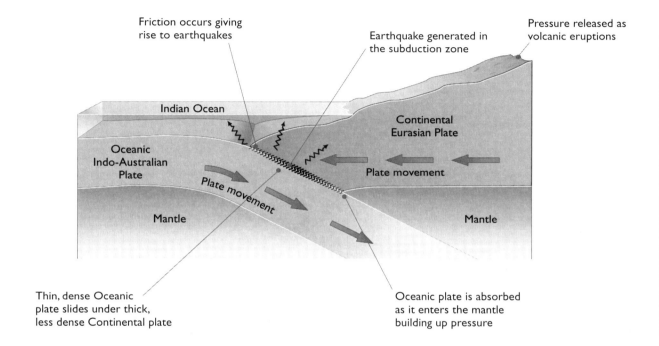

2.

Environmental effects	Economic effects	Social effects
The earthquake caused the entire Earth's surface to move vertically by a centimetre. The vast volumes of water pouring inland caused much of the coastline around the Indian Ocean to change shape.	The earthquake caused significant building damage on Sumatra particularly in the capital city of Banda Aceh even before the tsunami hit. Many coastal marine areas became polluted with dead bodies, debris and industrial waste as the retreating tsunami waves dragged them out to sea. The tsunami waves also destroyed vast areas of coral. Together these events have reduced tourist numbers and the money and jobs tourism brings.	Over a quarter of a million people were killed, a third of whom were children. Over one million people were left homeless. Coastal settlements in Indonesia and many in Thailand, Bangladesh, India and Sri Lanka were totally destroyed. The worst ever train disaster was caused by the tsunami in Sri Lanka as a train running along the western coast of the island was washed away by a wave killing over 1700 people. In the weeks after the tsunami, water-borne diseases such as cholera and typhoid spread due to the lack of fresh drinking water and sanitation.

3. Pupils should include details of the following in their account:

The earthquake caused the land to shake violently for up to 10 minutes causing significant building damage on Sumatra particularly in the capital city of Banda Aceh even before the tsunami hit.

A series of four major tsunamis were triggered creating waves that at some points reached a height of 30 metres when they reared up at the coastline and spilled as far as 2 kilometres inland

Over a quarter of a million people were killed a third of whom were children.

Dead bodies, debris and industrial waste were dragged out to sea as the tsunami waves retreated.

The tsunami waves destroyed vast areas of coral.

4. The **Richter scale** is a scale measuring the strength of an earthquake.

    The **epicentre** of an earthquake is the point on the Earth's surface directly above the focus of the earthquake.

    Liquefication is the break up of the ground into smaller pieces during an earthquake causing buildings to sink and collapse.

    A **natural disaster** is the result of a natural danger such as a volcano, earthquake, flood or hurricanes.

5. In November 2008, an early warning system was set up in Indonesia to give the people who live on vulnerable coastlines time to evacuate to higher ground, although officials have said that it will take several years to be fully effective.

    All Indian Ocean countries are developing evacuation procedures which are rehearsed regularly.

    Planning laws are being introduced for some buildings to have ground floors as car parks.

Extension question

6. Pupils' answers will vary but should be based on the following premise:

    LEDCs do not have the money to invest in methods of tectonic prediction such as monitoring seismic activity. Nor do they have the money or human resources to deal effectively with the aftermath of natural disasters where the longer-term effects such as contamination of water supplies and the spread of disease can be significantly more deadly than the event itself.

3.3 Case study: Volcano in an MEDC, Mount Etna, Sicily 2001

Exercise 3C

1.

Deformation of Mount Etna as magma rises.

↓

This movement of magma changes the shape of Etna causing the south side to bulge.

↓

Many earthquakes felt on 13th July.

↓

Magma pushes its way up and through the volcanoes vents.

↓

Ash and volcanic bombs ejected on 17th July.

↓

Huge plumes of ash soared from the crater.

↓

Volcanic bombs and lava flows all continued for the next 24 days.

↓

Lava flows in direction of Nicolosi.

↓

Lava destroyed roads, a scientific research station, a cable car and many ski lifts. The ash in the atmosphere and ash fall on the runway forced Catania airport to close.

2. Ash fall in the days and weeks after the eruption covered many of the vineyards that lined the slopes of Mount Etna, damaging or destroying the vines.

    The lava flows from the 2001 eruption caused extensive damage to ski facilities that needed to be quickly repaired before the beginning of the winter season. The warm lava fields that were left on Etna's slopes in the following months meant that snow found it hard to settle the following winter, impacting upon the tourist income generated from skiing.

    Ash or tephra fell for several miles around the volcano covering the city of Catania. The total cleaning cost to the city was estimated at over half a million pounds but the overall economic cost to Sicily has been much higher.

    The 2001 eruption of Mount Etna was highly publicised, with television crews reporting live from Etna's slopes. Many tourists cancelled their holidays to Sicily and even Italy as a result.

3. Scientific equipment can be used to predict when eruptions are likely to happen. Seismometres can be used to record changes in the shape of a volcano, instruments can be used to measure any increase in sulphur dioxide or carbon dioxide emissions and satellite imaging can show temperature changes on the slopes of a volcano. In preparation for a volcano, residents within mapped danger areas can be drilled in evacuation procedures.

4. Pupil's drawings will vary but should be along the lines of the sketch map below.

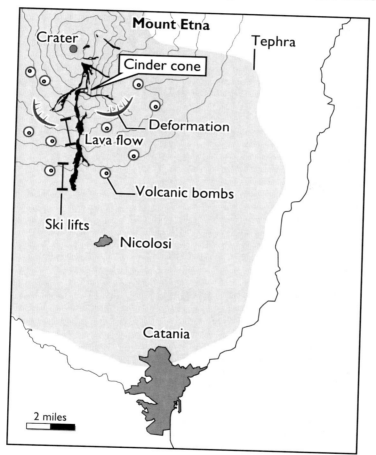

5. A **pyroclastic flow** is a fast-moving cloud of boiling gas ejected from a volcano. It is dangerous because it can travel at up to 200 km/hour, can spread out many kilometres from the volcanic cone and destroys everything in its path.

    A **lahar** is a mudflow that is created when rainwater or melting snow mixes with ash after a volcanic eruption. It is dangerous because it can flow down valleys, covering the area with several metres of mud.

Extension question

6. Tectonically active areas offer some distinct advantages to those living in them. The slopes surrounding volcanoes are ideal for farming because the soil is fertilised by the minerals weathered from the ash and solidified lava of previous eruptions. In the long term, eruptions benefit farming communities such as the vineyards that cover the lower slopes of Mount Etna.

   Volcanoes, and volcanic activities such as geysers, are increasingly attracting tourists, which creates a large service industry in such locations in the way of hotels, etc. Tourism is a large industry in New Zealand and Iceland partly for this reason.

   In LEDCs where the population is often very poor, the advantage of farming the fertile slopes of volcanoes may outweigh the risk of death or injury from the effects of an eruption. Also, populations and their governments in LEDCs may not be aware of the location of fault lines that may give rise to earthquakes.

   More able pupils may have further examples such as the following:

   Lucrative mining industries are also often found close to volcanoes as previous eruptions may have laid down seams of minerals such as silver. The easily accessible heat source close to the earth surface at plate boundaries can be used to create geothermal energy, a cheap and clean renewable form of energy.

3.4 Living with the threat, and responding to the hazards, of earthquakes and volcanoes

Exercise 3D

1. A volcano will begin to deform as the magma rises within it. This deformation can be seen by the naked eye but is more accurately monitored by satellites (and tiltmeters).

   Scientists can place sensing equipment on and around the volcano to measure the levels of sulphur dioxide and carbon dioxide being emitted by the volcano. A significant rises in the levels of these gases could mean an eruption is imminent.

   Seismometers, instruments that measure earthquakes, can be placed on the slopes of a volcano. Before an eruption many earthquakes will occur as the volcano begins to change shape.

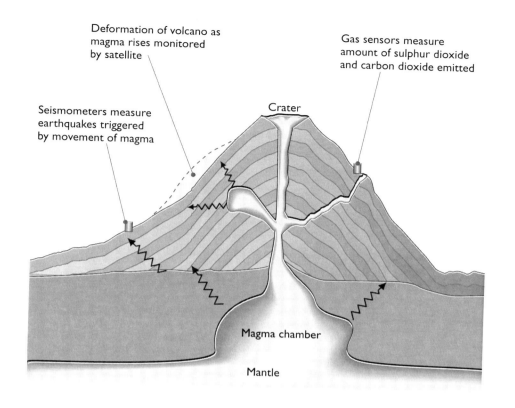

Deformation of volcano as magma rises monitored by satellite

Gas sensors measure amount of sulphur dioxide and carbon dioxide emitted

Seismometers measure earthquakes triggered by movement of magma

Crater

Magma chamber

Mantle

2. Pupil's drawings will vary but could include the following annotations:
    metal cross bracing
    rubber foundation
    sprinkler systems
    reinforced glass
    counter weight

3. A **foreshock** is a smaller earthquake coming before a bigger or main earthquake.

    Pancaking is the term used to describe a building collapsing during an earthquake.

    Seismographs are the machines that draw line graphs to illustrate the strength of earthquakes based on readings from seismometers.

    Deformation is the change in shape or bulging of a volcano just before it erupts. It is caused by rising magma.

4. Despite scientific development it remains extremely difficult to predict accurately where and when an earthquake may occur, other than expecting them to occur on plate boundaries. Animals can sense foreshocks and it has been observed that at times radon gas is emitted shortly before an earthquake, however these are uncertain methods of prediction which give little time for action. It remains much easier to prepare for an earthquake by building appropriately strong buildings and preparing evacuation and rescue plans.

5. In LEDCs we find that many thousands of people can be killed in earthquakes when they strike densely populated areas because they cannot afford to prepare their buildings to withstand earthquakes. Often, buildings in LEDCs are hastily built without following proper building regulations and consequently fall in on themselves (pancaking) even after small earthquakes. MEDCs can better afford to protect to their buildings to limit the damage and threat to life that earthquakes can cause.

Extension question

6. Answers should confirm this statement referring to the slow build up of signs that indicate a volcanic eruption may be likely to occur (deformation/satellite temperature mapping/gas emissions) compared to the inaccurate and irregular indicators used to predict earthquakes (animal activity/radon gas release/mapping of previous earthquakes along fault lines).

   Various examples could be used. For example, Mount Etna displayed typical slow build up signs before its eruption in 2001 with rumbling and releasing stream in the days before its eruption. Foreshocks and deformation were also evident before the main eruptions began on 13th July. In contrast, for the earthquake and resulting tsunami that devastated much of the Indian Ocean on 26th December 2004, there was no warning whatsoever other than animal activity.

Chapter 4: Economic activities

4.1 Putting jobs into different categories

Exercise 4A

1. **Primary**
   Farmer
   Oil drill operator

   Secondary
   Car assembly worker
   Textile factory worker
   Builder

   Tertiary
   Fireman
   Lawyer
   Professional footballer
   Dentist

   Quaternary
   Research scientist
   Inventor

2. (a) Quaternary
   (b) Primary
   (c) Secondary
   (d) Tertiary

3. (a) Multiple answers possible, e.g. pasture farm (062462)
   (b) Multiple answers possible, e.g. industrial estate (045443)
   (c) Multiple answers possible, e.g. hospital (045489)

4. Pupils may refer to some of the following industries:
   Primary: farms, woodland plantations, quarries, mines
   Secondary: industrial estates, factories
   Tertiary: hospitals, schools, train stations, sports centres, post offices, public houses

5. (a) Globalisation is the process by which companies, products, ideas and lifestyles are spread around the world.
   (b) Pupils should include two of each of the following:

Positive:

1. A reduction in trade taxes means that companies in LEDCs find it easier to trade their products with other LEDCs and more recently with MEDCs.

2. Huge improvements in transport and the demand for global holiday destinations from people in MEDCs mean that many LEDCs are now generating a high income from tourism. For example, many Asian and African countries such as Thailand and Egypt generate money from tourists through a tourist tax paid to the government. This is then invested in developing facilities which the local population require such as schools, roads and hospitals.

3. Many transnational companies have decided to locate their factories in LEDCs, which provides jobs for local people who may otherwise be unemployed.

Negative:

1. Governments in LEDCs have often encouraged the growth of industry without considering the environmental effects. China, for example, contains 16 out of the 20 most polluted cities in the world.

2. Some transnational companies have purposely located their factories in LEDCs so they can exploit low wages in these countries thereby increasing the company profits. Often factory workers are in fact paid below the average wage, and forced to work very long hours in poor conditions where they may not have access to drinking water. In some factories child labour is used, which is illegal.

3. The rapid increase in transnational factories locating in LEDCs means that many LEDCs are becoming dependent on these companies for jobs. Many local people, who may have previously worked for local companies or as farmers, take jobs with TNCs.

Extension question

6. Pupils' answers should include the following:

Transnational companies often locate their manufacturing sector in LEDCs to take advantage of cheap labour and other favourable conditions such as the reduced level of tax that is payable in some LEDC countries.

4.2 Examples of primary, secondary and tertiary activities (industries)

Exercise 4C

1. (a) **Arable** farming is mostly located in the south east of Britain.

   Pastoral farming generally occurs in the north west of Britain. Many farms have a mixture of these two types.

   (b) **Arable** farming is mostly located in the south east of Britain because the land is relatively flat with fertile soil which means it is suitable for growing crops and harvesting them with modern machinery. The south east receives sufficient rainfall for the crops to grow but not be flooded and receives more days of sunshine than other regions of Britain which helps crops grow.

   Pastoral farming generally occurs in the north west of Britain because it is not suitable for growing crops due to the steep relief, thin soils and wet, cold and windy climate. These physical conditions are acceptable for rearing animals however, particularly sheep which can graze on the mountainous slopes in the north west of Britain.

2. **Intensive farming** is a method of farming in which a lot of money is spent on machinery and labour; it usually takes places on a small scale such as market gardening and is often close to urban areas.

   Extensive farming is a method of farming in which less money is spent on machinery and labour; it usually takes place on a large scale such as a sheep farm.

   Subsidies are financial help given to farmers to guarantee a minimum income.

   A **surplus** is spare food created from agricultural overproduction.

   The **set-aside** scheme is a European Union initiative created to prevent overproduction of food in Europe. Farmers are paid not to farm on part of their land.

   Subsistence agriculture is a method of faming in which farmers grow only enough food to feed the family, pay taxes and perhaps provide a small surplus to sell.

3.

Location factor	Example industry
Close to raw materials	Stone mason
Near a skilled labour supply	Computer software development
Close to the market	Fruit processing factory
Large and flat site for a factory	Large car manufacturing plant

4. (a) This is because secondary industries manufacture goods made from raw materials that need to be brought to the factory by road or imported by cargo ship. After the secondary industry has manufactured the goods, they will need transporting to local, national or international tertiary industries.

    (b) Nearly all locations in Britain and within most MEDCs are connected to nationwide electricity grids. A source of power such as a fast-flowing river used to be important to industries that developed during the Industrial Revolution before the invention of the national grid.

5. (a) Fig. 4.2.2 shows that there has been a rapid and consistent growth in tourism from 1950 to 2004 when the total number of tourists reached 703 million. The graph also estimates that the growth in tourism will become even more rapid in the next 16 years reaching a figure of 1.6 billion by 2020. Tourism is greatest in Europe and very limited in South Asia, the Middle East and Africa, although it is projected that future growth will be quite good in South East Asia.

    (b) The rapid growth in tourism is a result of improvements in transport such as the construction of the Channel Tunnel as well as the availability and affordability of low-cost airline flights within, and now beyond, Europe.

6. The aeroplanes which bring tourists from other countries cause pollution problems. This may be overcome by adding a tax to airfares which will encourage tourists to use other forms of more environmentally friendly transport, such as train, to get to their resort.

    Sometimes large sections of land that are the habitat and breeding ground for a variety of animals are built upon, resulting in the loss of these animals. This problem can be overcome if the local government apply strict planning laws to limit development.

    Litter is a problem, especially in the larger tourist centres, and can take many hundreds or thousands of years to biodegrade. This may be overcome by providing litter bins and possibly fining individuals who litter.

Extension questions

1. Multiple answers are possible but any answer should be based on the following premise and be illustrated with examples:

    Secondary industries such as textile production began during the Industrial Revolution when mass production became possible. Power was supplied to manually controlled machines from a water wheel or by burning coal, so these industries had to locate near a fast-flowing river or coal field which were typically found in the north of Britain.

In the 20th century, secondary industries began to develop automatic machines to produce lighter products, and more recently hi-tech products. The development of the national grid meant that locating near a power source was no longer necessary and transport access has become more of an important location factor.

Some secondary industries are heavily influenced by one particular location factor such as a masonry factory, which needs to be near its raw material.

2. This answer requires some external research into tourism in LEDCs such as Egypt, Vietnam, Sri Lanka, etc. which may be internet-based. In their answer pupils should consider the economic benefit of tourism in these locations but also show awareness of their environmental impact.

4.3 Case study: The Toyota car plant at Burnaston

Exercise 4D

1. Britain has a large **market** for cars therefore many cars that would be manufactured in Britain would be sold in Britain. Britain already had many **component factories** that could supply a Toyota factory with the parts they needed. Britain also had a history of car manufacturing therefore had **skilled labour** to work in its factory. Despite being an island in the northern part of Europe Britain does in fact have excellent **transport** links to the rest of Europe.

2.

Labels should include:

Burnaston, near Derby, is centrally located in Britain and served well by the M6 and M1 motorways.

There are many component factories located in the West Midlands which could supply a Toyota factory.

Land in Derbyshire is relatively cheap.

The land is flat and even after the factory had been built there was still room for expansion.

3. **Labour** is the word to describe people who are employed by an industry.

The **Industrial Revolution** was a period of history when people left the countryside to work in factories in towns and cities.

Hi-tech goods are lightweight telecommunications and computer equipment such as mobile phones, MP3 players and laptop computers.

Science parks are developments of offices, industrial units and leisure facilities close to universities and good transport links.

4. During its most productive period, Toyota employed 2,850 people which has helped reduced unemployment in the local area and provides school leavers with a possible career. These workers are provided with very favourable working conditions which has helped to create a stable and happy workforce. Toyota's decision to locate its plant in the West Midlands has encouraged the development of further component manufacturers in the area which has been good for the local economy.

   NB during the current downturn in the car manufacturing industry, pupils should be aware that the situation at Toyota may have changed.

5. Advert should include some of the following:

   Generous shift allowance

   Paid overtime

   25 days' paid annual holiday (plus bank holidays)

   Private healthcare

   Pension

   Life assurance

   Attractive car plan

   Free workwear

   Subsidised restaurants

   Workplace nursery

Extension question

6. Pupils will have many ideas from their research and will include comments such as:

   Governments can do a number of things to attract MNCs such as Toyota to locate in their country. This may include reducing tax that foreign companies pay the government, providing a cash incentive to locate in a particular place called a grant and improving the transport system to make it a more attractive location for MNCs.

4.4 Case study: Nike textile supplier factories in South East Asia

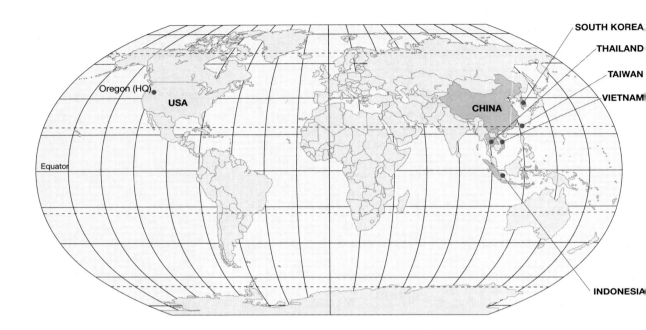

Location of Nike supplier factories and offices

(b) Pupils' answers will vary from their research but may include:

Gap – New Delhi, India

Starbucks – Guatamala

Adidas – Thailand

2. Pupils' answers will vary and may include any of the following. These are generic items regarding textile workers in LEDCs and may or may not apply to Nike's practices.

Textile workers in Vietnam may receive as little as $1.60 a day but a meal costs about 60–70 cents. This means they can only afford two meals per day and can barely afford a shelter.

Workers live in self-made housing along with the rest of their family. As many as 10 people may sleep, eat and wash in a one room hut.

Hundreds of workers work long hours in factories packed into a small space with little ventilation and scant access to drinking water, earning them the name sweatshops.

Many textile workers in Japan are only teenagers and are paid below the minimum wage.

Child labour is often used in countries such as Pakistan and Cambodia due to extreme poverty and little regulation by the government.

3. **Sweatshops**   Factories in LEDCs that pack many workers into a small space which often has little ventilation or a fresh water supply.

Labour intensive A process that requires lots of labour (e.g. textile manufacturing).

Regulation   Rules applied by companies or governments.

Living wage   A wage that will give an employee enough money for food and housing.

4. Pupils will need to research this question and may include some of the following:
   Gap in India have been investigated by the New Delhi authorities.
   Reebok have been investigated for some of their working practices.
   Adidas have been accused of human rights issues in Thailand.

5. (a) Nike has declared that, beginning in 2009, they will begin to provide minimum wages to their workers and full health insurance for every employee that is employed by the Nike Company. Nike has introduced a new policy called the Reuse-a-shoe which tries to ensure that material isn't wasted: old shoes are now ground up and made into a surface for a sports field or playground. Also, they are starting to use organic cotton and are aiming to recycle as much as possible. Nike has made a prototype shoe from recycled material to demonstrate what can be done with recycled materials.

   (b) Pupils' answers could include the following:
   - Prevent contractors using child labour
   - Inspect contractors factories to ensure workers have fresh water
   - Employ contractors in MEDCs not unregulated LEDCs

Extension question

6.   This is a subjective answer and will need some external research or teacher-led input. Possible suggestions for those responsible could include the following:
- National Governments
- International political organisations such as the EU (European Union) and UN (United Nations)
- Charities and pressure groups (Non-governmental Organisations – NGOs)

Measures to abolish unethical practices may include:
- Fining or prosecuting management executives in large TNCs for their role in encouraging unethical practices by using suppliers who are not regulated.
- Encouraging governments in LEDCs to introduce strict regulation concerning child labour, working hours and conditions within factories.
- NGOs may choose publicly to highlight examples of unethical practices by TNCs in the press which may embarrass them and lead to change.

Chapter 5: Location knowledge

5.1 Where in the world?

Exercise 5A

1.   (a) A = Africa
        B = Asia
        C = Antarctica
    (b) E, because Greenland is not a continent

2.   (a) Atlantic Ocean
    (b) Indian Ocean

3.   (a) Himalayas
    (b) Asia
    (c) Mount Everest

4.   (a) River 1 is the Mississippi
    (b) River 3 is the Rhine
    (c) The River Amazon which is marked number 2

5.   (a) Africa
    (b) The River Nile

Exercise 5B: Test yourself

1. Antarctica
2. Amazon
3. Yangtze
4. Mississippi
5. Everest
6. Andes
7. Nile
8. Sahara
9. Asia
10. Himalayas

5.2 Lines of latitude and longitude

Exercise 5C

1. A = Tropic of Capricorn
    B = Arctic circle
    C = The Equator
    D = Antarctic circle
    E = Tropic of Cancer

2. (a) Tropic of Cancer = 23.5° north
        Tropic of Capricorn = 23.5° south
    (b) Generally the climate changes as you move significant distances north or
        south. For example the Equatorial climate around the equator gives warm and
        wet climatic conditions but much further north or south it cools.

3. (a) The Prime Meridian
    (b) 0°

4. Multiple answers are possible, for example:
    Europe: Paris – 48° north, 2° east
    Asia: Beijing – 39° north, 116° east
    Oceania: Canberra – 35° south, 149° east
    North America: Washington DC – 38° north, 77° west
    South America: Santiago – 33° south, 70° west

5. The International Date Line is not a straight line in order to avoid populated
    landmasses. This is because longitude has a very important influence on human
    life in that it defines the time zones we have created across the globe.

Exercise 5D: Test yourself

1. Latitude
2. Hemisphere
3. Ninety
4. Cancer
5. Zero
6. Capricorn
7. Equator
8. Artic circle
9. Tropics
10. Longitude

5.3 The British Isles

Exercise 5E

1. (a) Great Britain and Ireland
   (b) England, Wales, Scotland and Northern Ireland

2. (a) Line 2
   (b) Country = Republic of Ireland
      Capital = Dublin

3. (a) The Irish Sea
   (b) The English Channel
   (c) Scandinavia

4. (a) River X = The Thames
      City Y = London
   (b) The North Sea

5. (a) The North West Highlands and the Grampians
   (b) F

Exercise 5F: Test yourself

1. Cardiff
2. Severn
3. North
4. UK
5. Great Britain
6. Edinburgh
7. Trent
8. Grampians
9. Belfast
10. London

5.4 The European Union (EU) and other countries

Exercise 5G

1. (a) A = The Republic of Ireland
   B = Italy
   C = Czech Republic
   D = The Netherlands
   E = Greece
   (b) A = Dublin
   B = Rome
   C = Prague
   D = Amsterdam
   E = Athens

2. (a) Warsaw
   (b) X

3. Country 1: Norway

4. (a) A = USA
   B = Egypt
   C = Peru
   D = China
   E = Australia
   (b) A = Washington DC
   B = Cairo
   C = Lima
   D = Beijing
   E = Canberra

5. 3

Exercise 5H: Test yourself

1. Copenhagen
2. Athens
3. Beijing
4. Portugal
5. Canberra
6. Cairo
7. Pakistan
8. New Delhi
9. Rome
10. Netherlands

Also available from Galore Park

English
Junior English 1
Junior English 1 Answers
Junior English 2
Junior English 2 Answers
Junior English 3
Junior English 3 Answers
So you really want to learn English 1
So you really want to learn English 1 Answers
So you really want to learn English 2
So you really want to learn English 2 Answers
So you really want to learn English 3
So you really want to learn English 3 Answers
English Practice Exercises 11+
English Practice Exercises 11+ Answers
English Practice Exercises 13+
English Practice Exercises 13+ Answers
English ISEB Revision Guide

Mathematics
Junior Maths 1
Junior Maths 1 Answers
Junior Maths 1 Teacher's Resource
Junior Maths 2
Junior Maths 2 Answers
Junior Maths 2 Teacher's Resource
Junior Maths 3
Junior Maths 3 Answers
So you really want to learn Maths 1
So you really want to learn Maths 1 Answers
So you really want to learn Maths 1 Worksheets
So you really want to learn Maths 2
So you really want to learn Maths 2 Answers
So you really want to learn Maths 2 Worksheets
So you really want to learn Maths 3
So you really want to learn Maths 3 Answers
So you really want to learn Maths 3 Worksheets
Mathematics Questions at 11+ Book A
Mathematics Questions at 11+ Book A Answer Book
Mathematics Questions at 11+ Book B
Mathematics Questions at 11+ Book B Answer Book
Mixed Maths Exercises Year 6 Pupil Book
Mixed Maths Exercises Year 6 Answers
Mixed Maths Exercises Year 7 Pupil Book
Mixed Maths Exercises Year 7 Answers
Mixed Maths Exercises Year 8 (Lower) Pupil Book
Mixed Maths Exercises Year 8 (Lower) Answers
Mixed Maths Exercises Year 8 (Upper) Pupil Book
Mixed Maths Exercises Year 8 (Upper) Answers
Mathematics ISEB Revision Guide
Mathematics Pocket Notes

Science
Junior Science 1
Junior Science 1 Answers
Junior Science 1 Teacher's Resource
Junior Science 2
Junior Science 2 Answers
Junior Science 2 Teacher's Resource
Junior Science 3
Junior Science 3 Answers
So you really want to learn Science 1
So you really want to learn Science 1 Answers
So you really want to learn Science 1
    Teacher's Resource
So you really want to learn Science 2
So you really want to learn Science 2 Answers
So you really want to learn Science 2
    Teacher's Resource
Science Pocket Notes – Living Things
Science Pocket Notes – Materials and Their
    Properties
Science Pocket Notes – Physical Processes

Geography
So you really want to learn Geography 1
So you really want to learn Geography 1 Answers
So you really want to learn Geography 2
So you really want to learn Geography 2 Answers
Geography ISEB Revision Guide
Revision Crosswords for Common Entrance and
    Scholarship Geography

History
Junior History 1
Junior History 1 Answers
Junior History 2
Junior History 2 Answers
Junior History 3
Junior History 3 Answers
So you really want to learn History 1
So you really want to learn History 1 Answers
So you really want to learn History 2
So you really want to learn History 2 Answers

Religious Studies
Religious Studies for Today
Bible Stories for Today
Religious Studies ISEB Revision
Preparing for Common Entrance Religious Studies

Also available from Galore Park

Classics
So you really want to learn Latin I
So you really want to learn Latin I Answers
So you really want to learn Latin II
So you really want to learn Latin II Answers
So you really want to learn Latin III
So you really want to learn Latin III Answers
So you really want to learn Latin Translations
Latin Prep 1
Latin Prep 1 Answers
Latin Prep 1 Audio
Latin Prep 2
Latin Prep 2 Answers
Latin Prep 3
Latin Prep 3 Answers
Latin Prep 1 Workbook A
Latin Prep 1 Workbook B
Latin Prep 1 Workbook Answers
Latin Puzzles
Latin Practice Exercises Level 1
Latin Practice Exercises Level 1 Answers
Latin Practice Exercises Level 2
Latin Practice Exercises Level 2 Answers
Latin Practice Exercises Level 3
Latin Practice Exercises Level 3 Answers
Nil Desperandum
Latin Galore
Ab Initio – A Latin Reference Grammar
Latin Vocabulary for Key Stage 3 and
      Common Entrance
Latin Flash Cards
A Latin Revision Reference for Common Entrance
      Level 1
A Latin Revision Reference for Common Entrance
      Level 2
The Jason Story – A Latin Reader
A Taste of Latin Poetry
Greek – A New Guide for Beginners

French
So you really want to learn French I
So you really want to learn French I Answers
So you really want to learn French I Audio
So you really want to learn French I Assessment Pack
So you really want to learn French 2
So you really want to learn French 2 Answers
So you really want to learn French 2 Audio
So you really want to learn French 2 Assessment Pack
So you really want to learn French 3
So you really want to learn French 3 Answers

So you really want to learn French 3 Audio
Skeleton French
French Vocabulary for Key Stage 3 and
      Common Entrance
Common Entrance French Grammar Handbook

Spanish
So you really want to learn Spanish I
So you really want to learn Spanish I Teacher's Book
So you really want to learn Spanish I Audio
So you really want to learn Spanish I Assessment Pack
So you really want to learn Spanish 2
So you really want to learn Spanish 2 Teacher's Book
So you really want to learn Spanish 2 Audio
So you really want to learn Spanish 3
So you really want to learn Spanish 3 Teacher's Book
So you really want to learn Spanish 3 Audio
Spanish Vocabulary for Key Stage 3 and
      Common Entrance

German
German Vocabulary for Key Stage 3 and
      Common Entrance
Und Du?

Study Skills
Study Skills – The complete guide to smart learning

Phonics
Step by Step Reading

Learning Together Verbal and Non Verbal Reasoning
How to do Verbal Reasoning – A Step by Step Guide
Preparation for 11+ and 12+ Tests:
      Verbal Reasoning – Book 1
Preparation for 11+ and 12+ Tests:
      Verbal Reasoning – Book 2
Preparation for 11+ and 12+ Tests:
      Verbal Reasoning – Book 3
Preparation for 11+ and 12+ Tests:
      Verbal Reasoning – Book 4
Verbal Reasoning Challenge Tests
How to do Non Verbal Reasoning –
      A Step by Step Guide
Preparation for 11+ and 12+ Tests:
      Non Verbal Reasoning – Book 1
Preparation for 11+ and 12+ Tests:
      Non Verbal Reasoning – Book 2

Galore Park
ISEB EXAM PAPERS

GALORE PARK

Why ISEB Exam Papers?

- Perfect for 11+, 13+ and scholarship entrance exam preparation

- Provides practice on papers used in previous exams so that pupils familiarise themselves with the exam format prior to the exam

- Enables pupils to see the type of question asked in the exam as well as the level of difficulty so that they can adequately prepare

- Answers also available so that pupils can check whether they have answered correctly or need to do further revision

Galore Park
ISEB REVISION GUIDES

GALORE PARK

English
ISEB Revision Guide

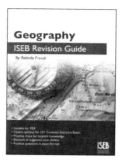

Geography
ISEB Revision Guide

Science
ISEB Revision Guide

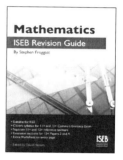

Mathematics
ISEB Revision Guide

Why ISEB Revision Guides?

- Perfect for 11+, 13+ and scholarship entrance exam preparation

- Consolidates the key information for the subject area into ONE resource making revision a breeze!

- Enables pupils to identify gaps in knowledge so that they can focus their revision

- Worked examples help pupils to see how they can gain the best possible marks

- Each guide includes a small amount of practice material and the answers to test understanding

- All guides are fully up to date with the latest syllabus changes to ensure pupils are revising the correct material

Independent Schools
Examinations Board

Galore Park
STUDY SKILLS

GALORE PARK

Why Study Skills?

- Perfect for any pupil aged 8–13

- Packed full of lots of practical advice about how to revise and how to be a smarter learner

- Enables pupils to identify their learning style so that they can revise using the techniques that work for them

- Includes plenty of examples of revision techniques such as mind maps and memory games which will help pupils to retain information more easily

- Workbook format enables pupils to keep a learning log which they can keep referring back to